GOD CREATES A SNAKE

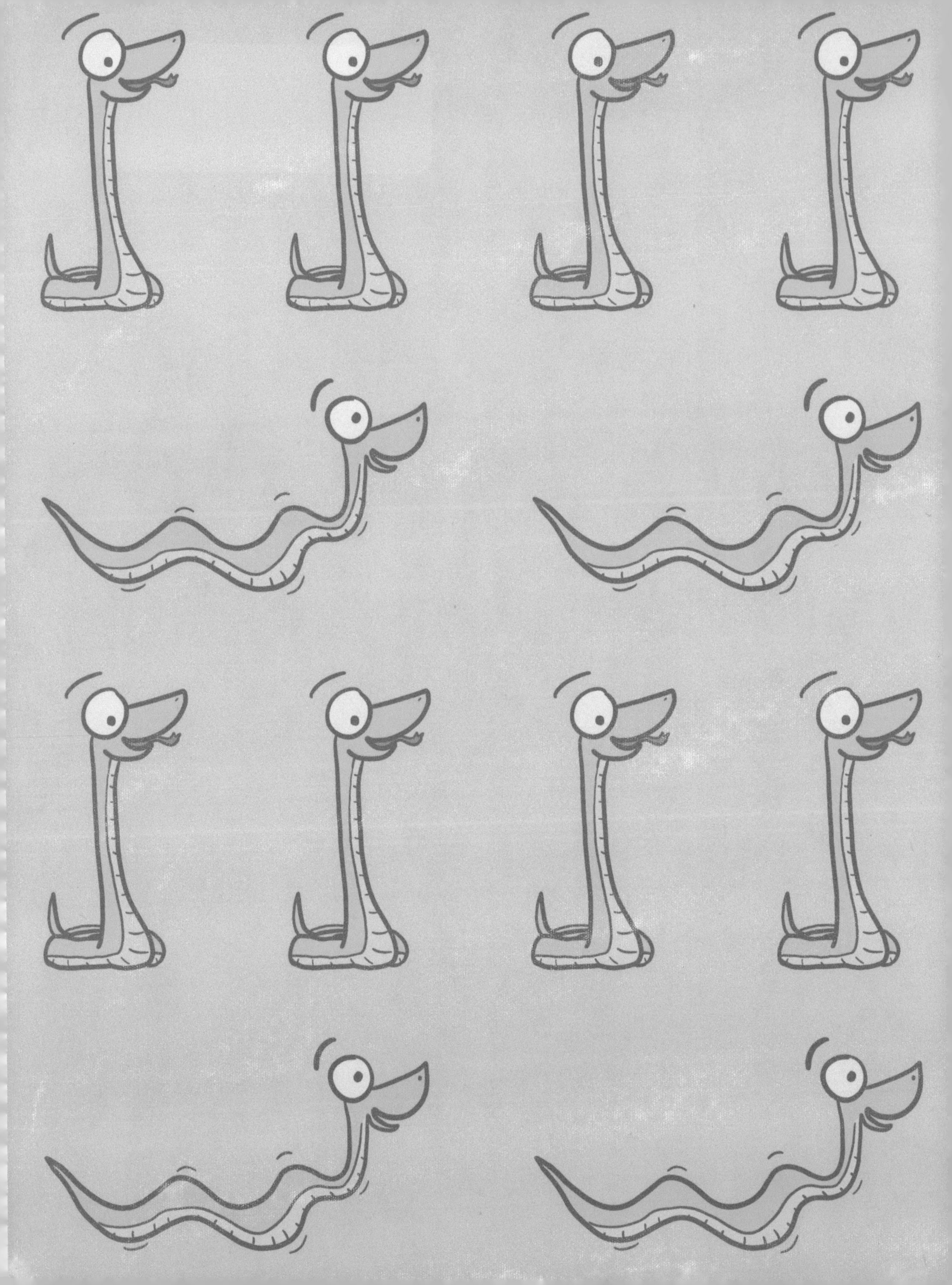

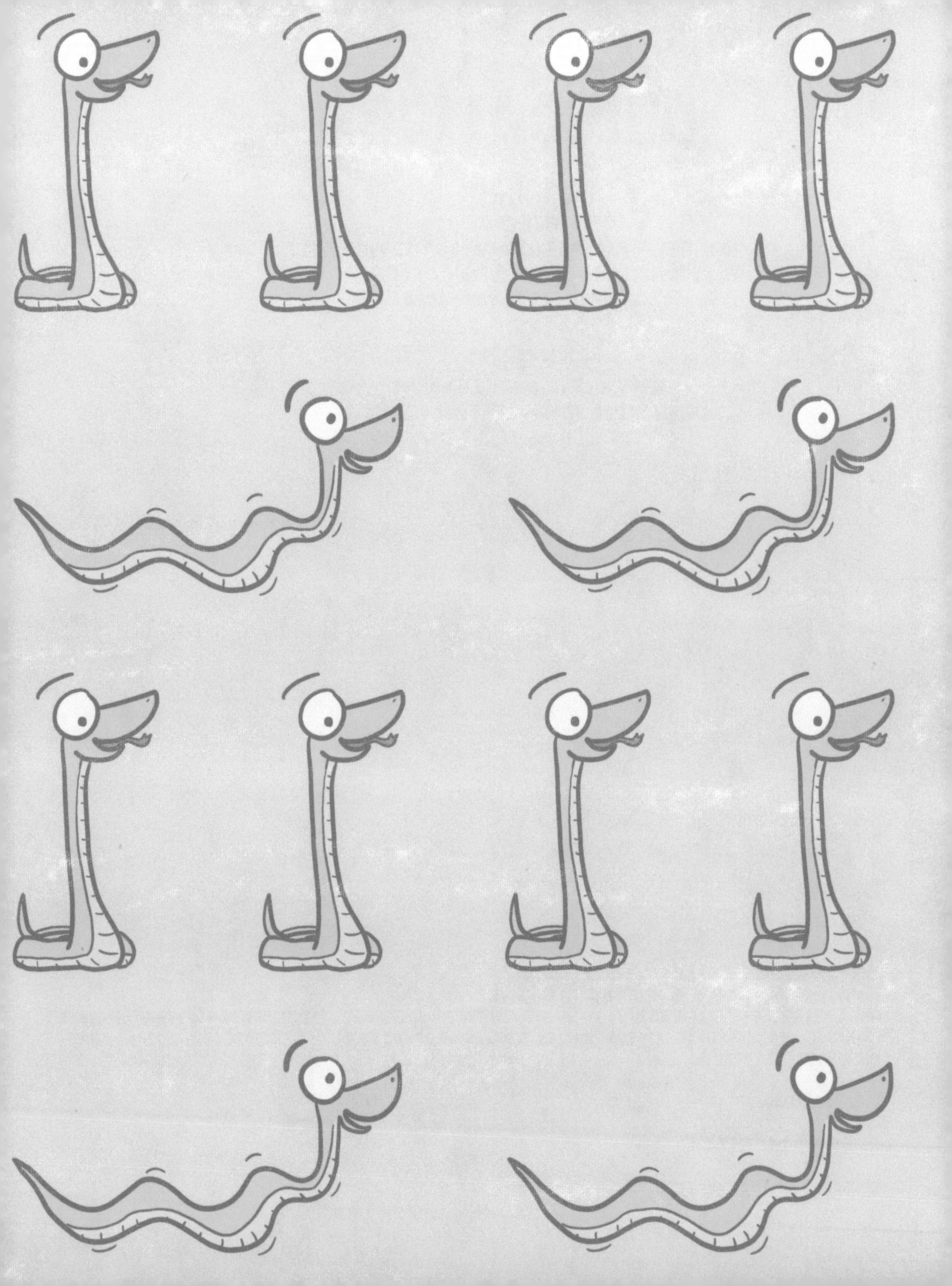

DEDICATION

CHARLES:

TO MY WIFE AND KIDS,
YOU ARE THE REASON I DO WHAT I DO. I LOVE YOU.
TO EVERYONE WHO EVER LAUGHED AT ONE OF MY JOKES...I LOVE YOU TOO.

BRIAN:

MARY, OLIVIA, NORA, AND DEAN:
THANK YOU FOR GROANING AT ALL MY JOKES.
IT FUELS ME. I LOVE YOU.

FIRST PRINTING, 2019

ISBN 978-0-9859277-3-8

WWW.GODCREATINGANIMALS.COM

GOD CREATES A SNAKE

CHARLES PETERSON

ILLUSTRATED BY BRIAN RUSSELL

CREATION STATION

SNAKE?
THE BOSS WILL SEE YOU NOW.

HEY LITTLE BUDDY, I'M ALMOST DONE CREATING YOU!

GREAT! WHAT CAN I DO SO FAR?

YOU CAN GO ON LAND...

YOU CAN CLIMB TREES...

AND YOU CAN SWIM IN WATER!

OMG
ARE YOU
SERIOUS?

PRETTY COOL, RIGHT?

YOU DIDN'T HAVE TO DO ALL THIS JUST FOR ME!

ANY OTHER QUESTIONS?

HOW FAST WILL I RUN?

WHAT?

I BET I'LL RUN SUPER FAST!

UHHH...

SO FAST ON
MY LEGS!

THEY DIDN'T TELL YOU I RAN OUT OF LEGS?

HOW DO YOU RUN OUT OF LEGS??

WELL--
WHAM

HEY GOD DO
I REALLY NEED
100 LEGS?

YOU WEREN'T SUPPOSED TO SEE THAT...

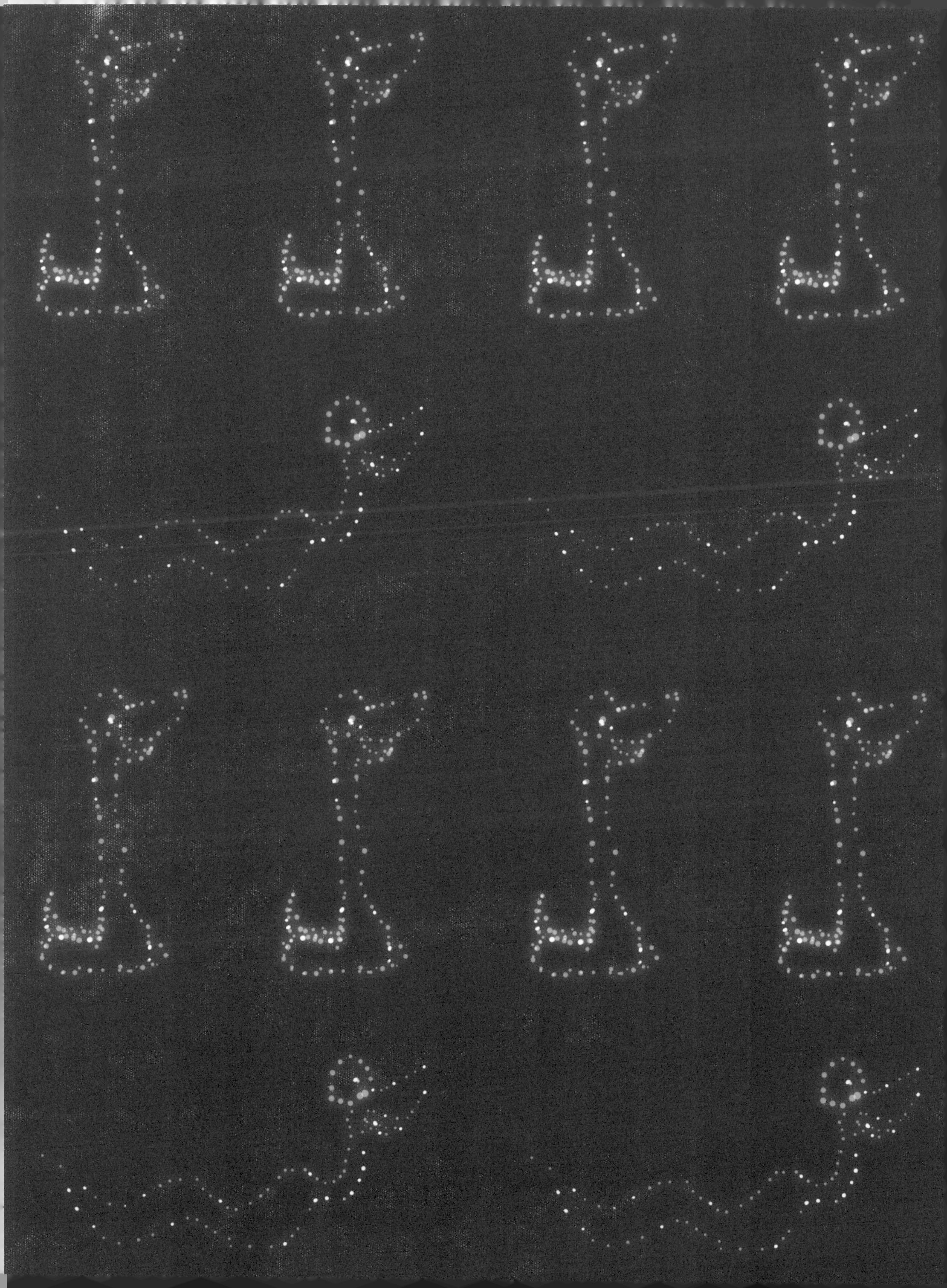

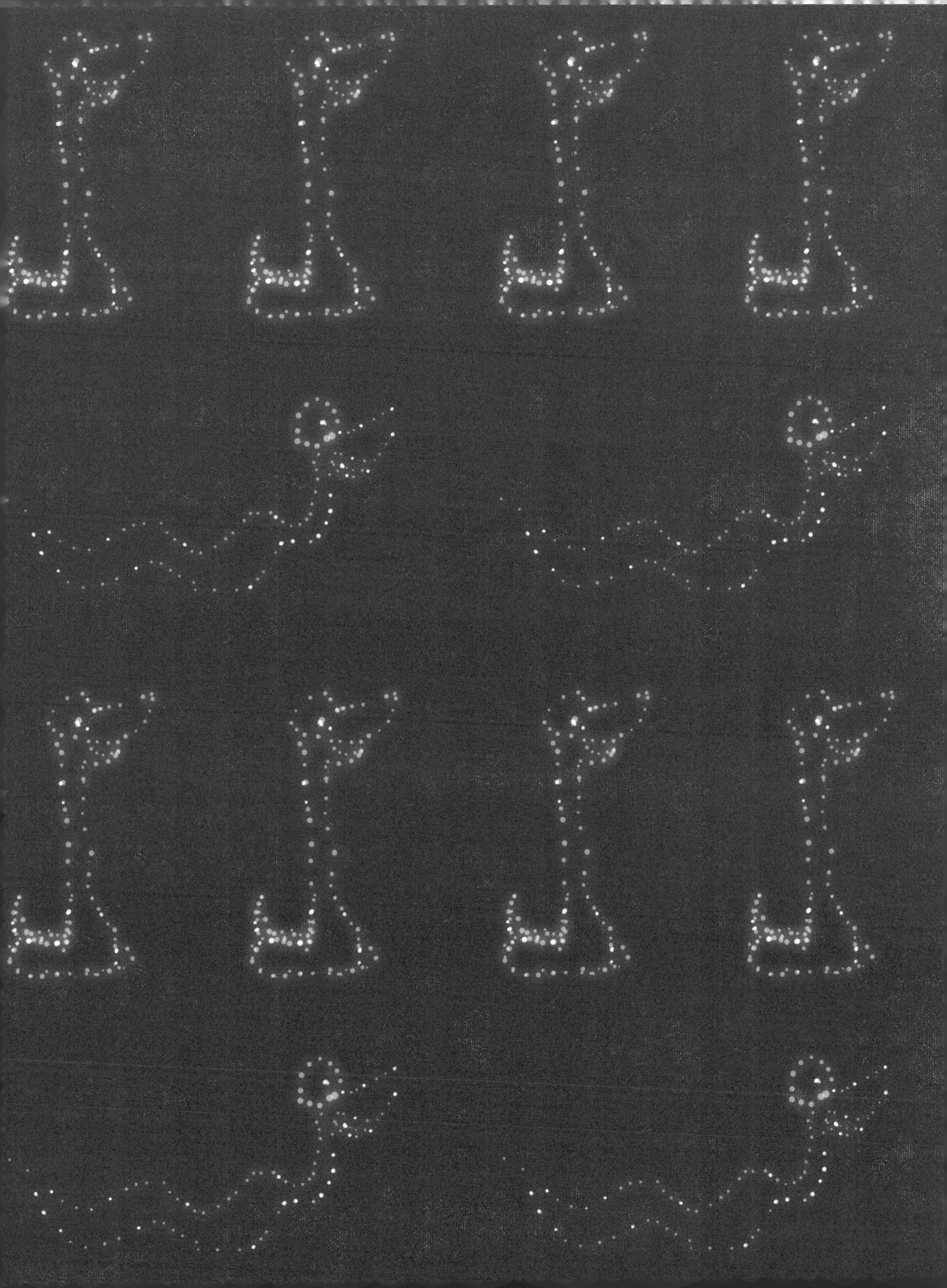

CPSIA information can be obtained
at www.ICGtesting.com
Printed in the USA
LVHW072140130819
627573LV00020B/294/P